No One For Games

Chris Culshaw

Oxford University Press

No One For Games

1
Five-a-side

When I was at school I loved playing five-a-side football. We had a training session every Friday after school. We usually had a match on Sunday morning against another local school. It was a great way to end the week. I was in a team with my four mates: Alan, Stuart, Matthew, and Phillip.

Our Games teacher was called Mr Lofthouse. He was only five feet tall. We called him Lofty – but not to his face! Lofty was a good teacher. He was very keen on five-a-side. So he came along every Friday to watch and help with our training.

2
At the Gym

One Friday, after school, I went to the gym as usual. My four mates were there already. 'Come on,' I said, 'time to get changed.'

Alan said, 'We can't.'

I asked them why not.

'We're injured,' said Stuart.

'What, all of you?' I said.

'Yes,' said Matthew, 'all of us.'

I couldn't believe it. They had all been fit the day before. 'What happened?' I asked.

Just then Lofty came in. 'Come on, you lot, you should be changed by now.'

I told Lofty that I was the only one who could play. He sat down on a bench, scratched his head and said, 'What's going on?'

3
What's Going On?

The others all started talking at once. Then they started to shout. In the end Lofty took out his whistle and blew it hard. 'Alan,' he said very quietly, 'you start. You three – keep quiet. Or I'll show you my yellow card.' Alan went red.

'Go on,' said Phillip, 'tell Sir all about your mouldy dog.'

Lofty looked at Phil and scowled. 'Shut up Phillip Longton. Or I'll send you off.'

We all laughed.

Alan said, 'Well Sir, it all started this morning. I was taking our Sparky for a run. I always take him for a run, every day before school. Well, Sparky saw Phillip Longton's bony old cat and ran after it. He pulls really hard on the lead. He's a big dog, Sir.'

'A big flea-bitten dog,' chipped in Phil.

Alan scowled, 'He pulled me right into the road and I fell over and hurt my ankle.'

Alan showed Lofty the bandage. 'That's why I can't play tonight, Sir.'

4
Stuart's and Matthew's Stories

Lofty said, 'Okay, that's one down and three to go. Who's next?'

'Me, Sir,' said Stuart. 'I was on my bike, coming down Church Street, on my way to school. All of a sudden Alan ran out in front of me. He was getting dragged along by his big brainless dog. I had to slam on the brakes and swerve. I almost killed the horrible hound.'

'You should have,' said Phil.

Stuart carried on, 'Well, I fell off my bike and bashed my knee, Sir.' He showed Lofty his bandage. 'That's why I can't play.'

'Whatever next!' said Mr Lofthouse with a grin. 'Two down and two to go. Who's next?'

Matthew was next. 'I was in Church Street as well, Sir. I saw it all. I saw Alan's bone-headed dog pull him into the road. I saw Stu fall off his bike. It was really funny. I was laughing so much I was crying. I wasn't looking where I was going and I...'

'And you what?' asked Mr Lofthouse.

'He walked straight into a lamp-post, Sir!' laughed Stuart. 'It was just like one of those old black-and-white films, wasn't it, Matt?'

Matthew showed Lofty a big bump on his head. 'I've been feeling a bit dizzy all day. I went to see the school nurse. She said I should give five-a-side a miss this week. That's why I can't play, Sir.'

5
What Happened to Phillip?

Lofty turned to Phillip. 'Well, Mr Longton – last but not least. What happened to you?'

'Yeah, go on, Phillip! Tell Sir what happened to you!' the others chanted.

Lofty beamed, 'I'm all ears, Phillip.'

Phil cleared his throat and began. 'I was trying to catch Sandy, my very expensive cat. We never let her out, Sir. Too many dogs down our street. But my dad left the back door open this morning and she ran off. I chased her up the road and saw Alan Clarke with his mouldy mongrel. You can guess what happened then, Sir – his horrible hound attacked my poor little Sandy.'

'No he didn't!' shouted Alan, 'Sparky wouldn't harm a fly.'

'Pipe down, Alan,' said Mr Lofthouse. 'Let him finish. Go on, Phillip.'

'Well, Alan fell into the road – serves him right too. Stu nearly ran over him. Then Matt tried to head-butt a lamp-post. It was like World War Three with bodies everywhere. Matt had flopped down on the pavement.'

'My head was spinning, Sir,' said Matthew.

'Like the time you kissed Sarah Bates?' said Alan.

Matthew blushed. 'I never kissed Sarah Bates. She kissed me.'

Lofty looked at his watch. 'Get on with it, Phillip.'

'Where was I?' said Phillip. 'Oh yes... Matt had flopped down on the pavement. I went over to see if he was all right. He was sitting on the pavement rubbing his head. His lunch-box had fallen out of his bag and his lunch was all over the place. I was helping him to pick it up when Sandy came along. And do you know what? She nicked Matt's lunch. She ran off with his tuna sandwich. She loves tuna, Sir.'

6
Cat Up the Tree

'So what did you do then, Phillip?' asked Lofty. 'Did you dial 999?'

'No, Sir,' said Phil, 'Alan came limping along and I asked him to help me catch Sandy. By this time she was up a tree. She just sat there, eating Matt's tuna sandwich.'

'I can see what's coming,' laughed Lofty. 'The fire brigade? The SAS?'

'No need for them, Sir,' beamed Phillip. 'We used teamwork – just like you teach us in PE. I got on Alan's shoulders and tried to grab Sandy.'

'He missed, of course,' chipped in Alan, 'got a handful of tuna and salad cream instead.'

'And did you know, Sir,' said Phillip, 'that killer bees just love salad cream? Go wild for it, they do.'

Mr Lofthouse looked at Phillip. 'Killer bees? Are you pulling my leg?'

Alan laughed. 'They were wasps, Sir. There was a wasps' nest in the tree.'

Phillip said crossly, 'They were bees, Sir! Killer bees. As big as golf balls. That's why I can't play, Sir. I got stung.'

'If they were killer bees,' said Matthew, 'how come you're still alive?'

Phillip didn't answer.

Matthew said, 'Anyway, show Sir where you got stung, Phillip!'

Phillip went very red. Lofty stood up, looked at his watch and said, 'Don't bother to show me, Phillip. I can guess.' He went to the door. 'So, no training tonight. I'll see you all next Friday – I hope.' He looked at me and winked. 'In the meantime, keep away from mad dogs, stray cats, lamp-posts, and, of course, killer bees.'

7
My Excuse

Next Friday we all met up again as usual. This time it was me who couldn't play. Alan, Stu, Phil, and Matt were all fit again. But I was injured.

Mr Lofthouse saw my bandaged hand and he roared with laughter. 'Killer bees or wild dogs?' he said.

'No, Sir.'

'Attacked by aliens disguised as lamp-posts?'

The others laughed.

'No, Sir,' I said at last. 'A hot-water bottle, a bike-pump, a sliced loaf, and my mum's wedding ring.'

Lofty grinned. 'Sit down, lads...this is going to be a long story.'

Oxford University Press, Walton Street, Oxford, OX2 6DP

Oxford New York
Athens Auckland Bangkok Bombay
Calcutta Cape Town Dar es Salaam Delhi
Florence Hong Kong Istanbul Karachi
Kuala Lumpur Madras Madrid Melbourne
Mexico City Nairobi Paris Singapore
Taipei Tokyo Toronto

and associated companies in
Berlin Ibadan

Oxford is a trade mark of Oxford University Press

ISBN 0 19 833490 7

Printed in Great Britain

Illustrations by Colin King